Highlights PUZZLEMANIA

Wyatt's TRY-ITS

Are you having trouble solving the CODE on page 19? Work on the shortest words first. It's easier to figure out a word when you only need to replace one or two letters.

Highlightskids.com

Check out the Highlights Kids website. It's awesome! You'll find tons more mind-bending puzzles, great games, and loads of jokes and riddles. And that's just the tip of the iceberg. There are also stories, articles, crafts, and much more. It's 100 percent Wyatt-approved!

Look Again!

Can you find 7 jigsaw pieces hidden on the cover?

Answer on page 30

Cover illustration by Dave Clegg

Namaste, Puzzlemaniacs!

Wyatt the Riot™ here, there, and everywhere! Are you ready for your latest batch of mind-bending super challenges? Then sharpen a pencil and start puzzling.

Don't forget to check out my blog. That's the sticker story on page 24. Find out what happens when I grab a [bat] and step up to home plate.

And be sure to take a look at my personal puzzle pick: "Peanut Gallery" on page 16. Olivia will love this one—she is really nuts about animals!

Over & out!

Wyatt

Find Your Favorites

Olivia has made a list of puzzles for you—as usual!

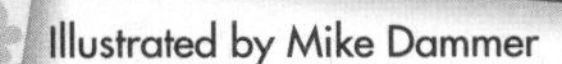
Illustrated by Mike Dammer

Start Your Engines

It's Tune-up Tuesday at Otto's Auto Shop. While these cars get checked, check to see if you can find at least 20 differences between these pictures.

Answer on page 30

Five are on this page.
Can you find them all?
Oil

PENCIL*PATHS
Answer on page 30
Which pencil wrote each word?
1
5
2
4
3

Word for Words

The letters in **SUBMARINE** can be used to make many other words. Use the clues below to come up with some of them. A flightless bird, for example, might make you think of the word EMU. See how many of the others you can guess.

Answer on page 30

S U B M A R I N E

1. **A flightless bird** E M U
2. **You might ride to school in this** ___ ___ ___
3. **A male sheep** ___ ___ ___
4. **Farm building** ___ ___ ___ ___
5. **Not far** ___ ___ ___ ___
6. **Umbrella weather** ___ ___ ___ ___
7. **Horse hair** ___ ___ ___ ___
8. **A flashlight ray** ___ ___ ___ ___
9. **Subtraction sign** ___ ___ ___ ___ ___
10. **Ambulance sound** ___ ___ ___ ___ ___
11. **He or she works with a doctor** ___ ___ ___ ___ ___
12. **1 is one** ___ ___ ___ ___ ___ ___

Wacky Workout

Time to exercise your eyes! There are some strange sights at the gym today. Can you find at least **25** odd, weird, or wacky things in this picture?

Illustrated by Peter Grosshauser

Nothing to It!

This zero is filled with a whole lot of nothing. Nineteen words or phrases that mean nothing are hidden up, down, across, backwards, and diagonally. Find them all, and you'll be second to none!

Answer on page 30

N V E U B
O V A C A N T
N O T H I N G J G
E C O M I S S I O N L
P R K N Z E R O
N N E N Z N H T
A I H A L O V E
D N P L Z O E D
A C I B I I M P
B M C L L I P U
V O I D S C S T
W T U O T U H S H T Y
X G G E E S O O G
I N A U G H T
N U L L Q

Word List

- ~~BLANK~~
- CIPHER
- EMPTY
- GOOSE EGG
- LOVE
- NADA
- NAUGHT
- NIL
- NIX
- NONE
- NOTHING
- NULL
- OMISSION
- SHUT OUT
- VACANT
- VOID
- ZERO
- ZILCH
- ZIP

Add a Letter

You can use the letter ***R*** to turn a boot into a robot. Take **BOOT** and add an **R**. Move the letters around to make **ROBOT**. Use your stickers finish the job. Then see if you can figure out the rest.

Answer on page 30

BOOT

+ R =

BEAR

+ Z =

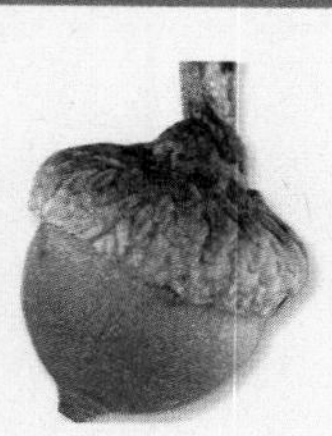

ACORN

+ Y =

MOLE

+ N =

SKATE

+ B =

BELT

+ A =

+ P =

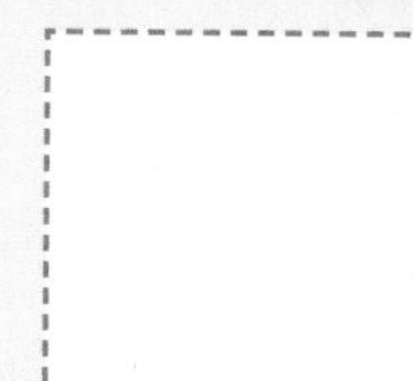

+ H =

+ T =

+ N =

Hidden Pictures®

Snow Kidding

There is more than meets the eye on this slope. Can you find the hidden objects?

Answer on page 30

Illustrated by Timothy Davis

book

crown

bottle

frog

paper clip

glove

hanger

goose

heart

fish

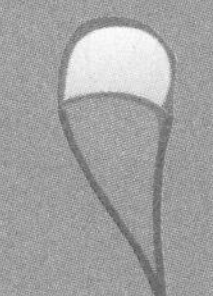

ice-cream cone

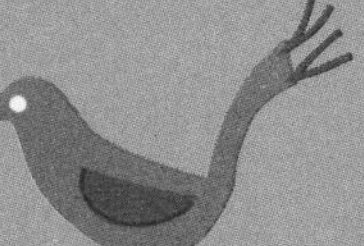

bird

saiboat

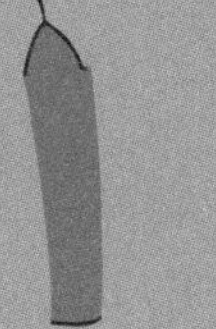

candle

bell

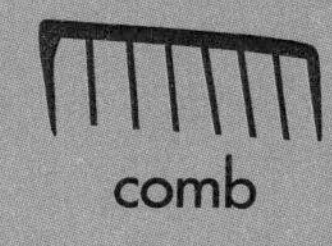

comb

baseball cap

tweezers

bat

star

slice of bread

banana

needle

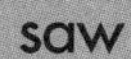

saw

State Your Name

Use the state nicknames to fill in this crossword two letters at a time. Each answer is a state abbreviation. We've filled in the first one. Can you deliver the rest?

Answer on page 31

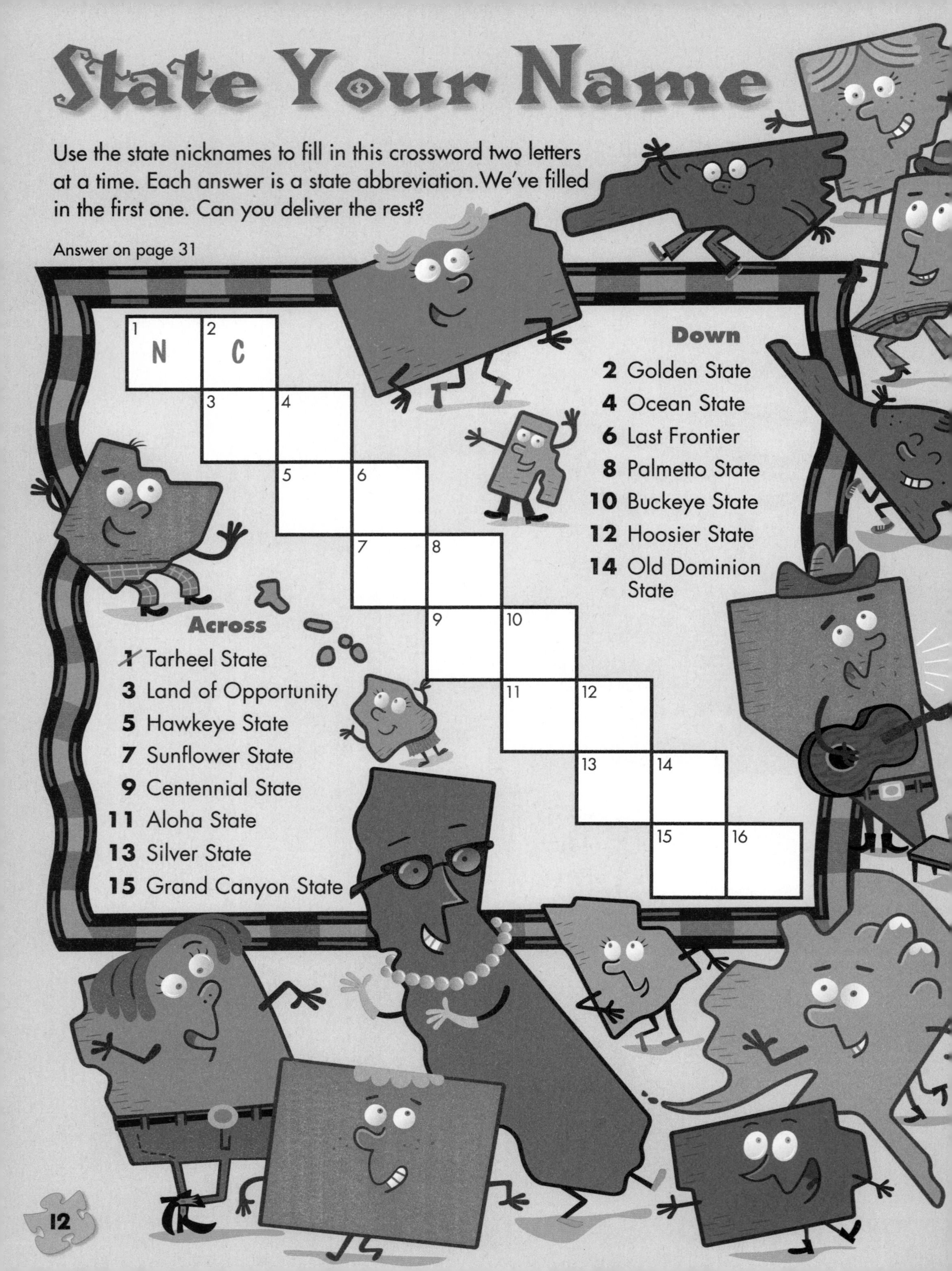

Across

~~1~~ Tarheel State
3 Land of Opportunity
5 Hawkeye State
7 Sunflower State
9 Centennial State
11 Aloha State
13 Silver State
15 Grand Canyon State

Down

2 Golden State
4 Ocean State
6 Last Frontier
8 Palmetto State
10 Buckeye State
12 Hoosier State
14 Old Dominion State

Math Mirth

The Math Club is holding its annual comedy night. Can you guess the answers to these riddles? All the letters you need are in the word list. Each fraction tells you which letters to use.

Answer on page 31

Disguise the Limit

Calling all detectives! Ten suspects are on the loose in Puzzlemania Park. Take a good look at the posters. Then see if you can find each suspect on the next page. Each is wearing the same clothes as on the wanted posters. Can you nab them all?

Answer on page 31

Illustrated by Tim Haggerty

Peanut Gallery

These elephants are cooling off. While they do, keep your cool and use your stickers to finish the picture. Then take a good look at the scene. There are 25 peanuts hidden here. Can you find them all?

Answer on page 31

Illustrated by Kevin Rechin

Map Mix-Up

People are flocking to Logicville for the big Summer Festival. Unfortunately, the new town maps were printed without labels on most of the buildings on Main Street. To help the lost tourists, read the clues below to figure out which building is which. Fill in the correct names on the map.

1. Archie's Arcade is one building south of the Sandwich Hut.
2. Izzy's Ice Cream is northeast of Archie's Arcade.
3. The Movie Palace is north of Sim's Sweets.
4. The T-Shirt Shack is one building south of Izzy's.

Answer on page 31

The Text Big THiNg

Maddie texts so much that her friends call her Thumbs. Her mom texted her some secret news. Can you help Maddie decipher the message? Each number stands for one of the letters that goes with that number on the keypad. For example, the first word is **HELLO**, with the **L** found on the **5** key, and the **O** found on the **6** key. Can you fill in the rest of the message?

Answer on page 31

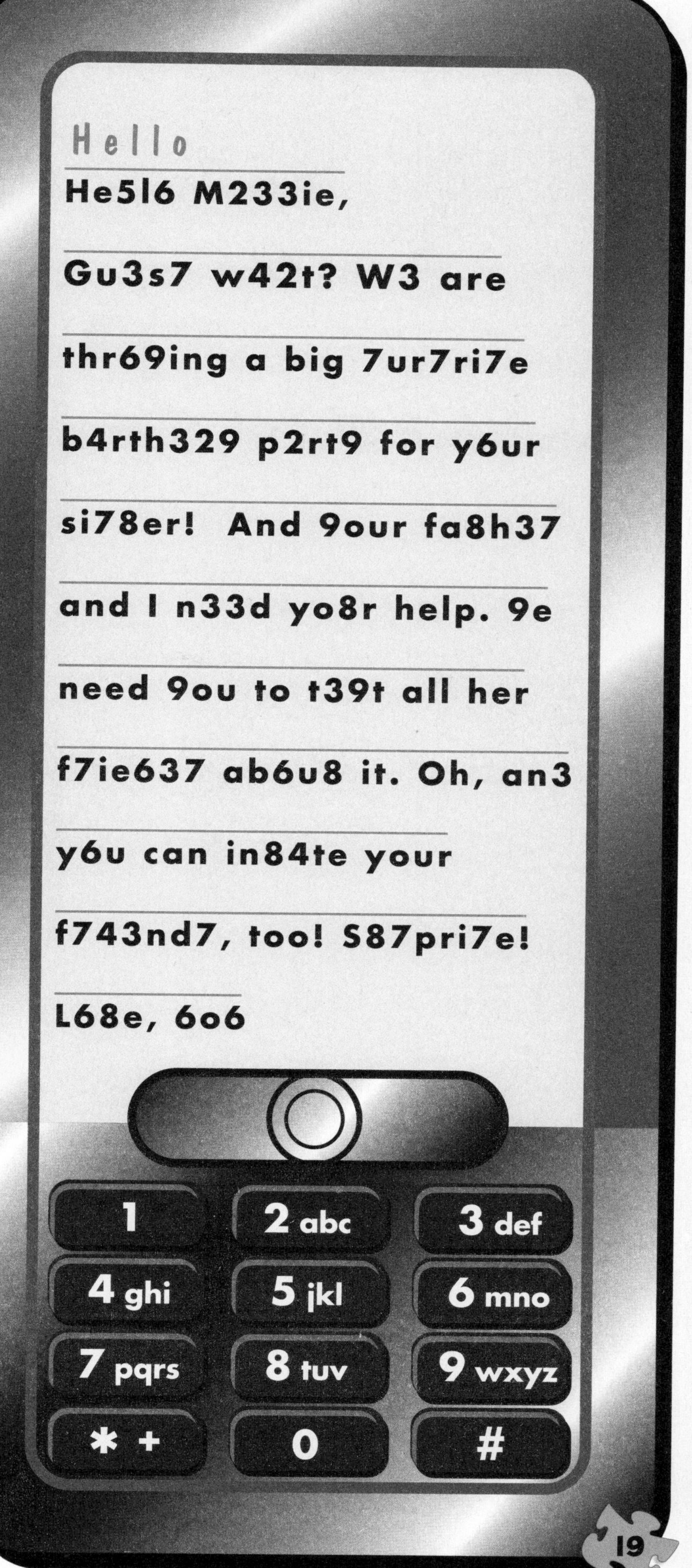

Veggie Q's

Answers on page 31

To Market, to Market

Help Ellie reach the farmers' market before it closes.

Start

Finish

Illustrated by Mike Moran

Veggies or Not?

Each pair of words has one veggie and one phony. Circle the veggies.

Kale or **Yale?**

Swedish Bard or **Swiss Chard**

Fennel or **Funnel?**

Oprah or **Okra?**

Jalapeño or **Jalopy?**

Wallaby or **Kohlrabi?**

Vegetable Soup

This bowl is swimming with veggies! Put together the parts to make the names of 4 vegetables.

ROOM EGG PUMP CAR

KIN ROT MUSH PLANT

____

____

____

____

Match Up

Can you find four differences between these two baskets?

Hidden Veggies

A vegetable is hidden in the letters of each sentence. Find **Y-A-M** in order in the first sentence. Then find a different veggie in each of the others.

Please try a marshmallow.

Could this be any sillier?

This décor needs to be updated.

An antelope ambled by.

That bee tried to sting me!

Far-out Food

On the planet Verdura the aliens who live there look a little like veggies. Can you add a face and other features to this picture to show someone from Verdura?

Feeling Antsy

This enchanting puzzle is crawling with ants! There are 30 ant words hidden in this grid. For each one the word *ANT* has been replaced by a picture of an ant. For example, **ANTELOPE** appears as **ELOPE**. Crawl up, down, across, backwards, and diagonally to find as many as you can.

Answer on page 32

Word List

~~antELOPE~~
antENNA
antIDOTE
antIQUE
antLERS
antSY
BRILLIant
CHant
CONSTant
CROISSant
DISTant
EGGPLant
ELEGant
ELEPHant
FantASY
FRAGRant
GALLant
GIant
HYDRant
IMMIGRant
IMPORTant
INFant
INSTant
PAGEant
PHEASant
SERGEant
SLant
TARantULA
VACant
Want

C	R	O	I	S	S		S	S	E	L	E	G		Z
	F		A	S	Y	L	N	F		Z	E	H	T	F
E	L	E	P	H		J	S	Z	R	C	P	S	S	R
L	U		D	D	F	W		G		O	A	P	I	A
O	Y	E	P		N	Z	U	A	S	Y		V	D	G
P	M	G	H	L	I	R		L	Y	Z	I	A	G	R
E	I	R	E	P	M	A	R	L	O		L	E	G	
E	N	E	A	G		N	G		S	I	L	E	U	B
U	S	S	S	G	E	N	I	C	C	E	I	E	T	M
Q	T	R		E	G	E	M	O	H	V	R	D	R	A
I		H	T	E	A		M	N	B	Y	B	S		S
		T	R	O	P	M	I	S	M	C	D	O	I	R
	I	D	O	T	E	C	I	T	Z	H	Y	R	G	A
T	A	R		U	L	A	X		I		H	S		Q

Illustrated by Dave Clegg

Wyatt's dad helped him set up a blog that friends like you can read. Wyatt shares the news. Then you add stickers to the spaces to turn his blog into a funny story.

Profile

Friends

Ike Howard

Anna Shaw

Isabel Vega

Lucas Vega

Max Patel

Olivia Rogers

Comments

Jake Rogers

A grand slam bunt! ☺

Wyatt at the Bat

Ever since I was little, I've liked baseball. I used to swing my STICKER in the backyard and pretend I was a famous slugger like Hank Aaron or Babe STICKER. In my imagination, I always hit a home run to win the championship STICKER.

Now I'm on a real team—the Purple STICKER. I play second base, Dad is the coach, and Jake helps out. Today's game was wild! The bases were loaded as I stepped into the batter's STICKER in the last inning. A home STICKER would win the game for real!

Jake was coaching third STICKER. I glanced his way and saw him scratch his nose. That was the signal to bunt.

The STICKER sent the ball toward home plate. As I choked

p on the bat, I heard Jake shout, "Wyatt, no!" But it was too late. I bunted.

It should have been an easy out, but the other team was taken by surprise. After a

ew seconds, the catcher picked up the STICKER and threw it—right over the first

aseman's STICKER . By the time the outfielder chased it down, the other runners were

, and I was sliding into home. SAFE! Everyone poured onto the STICKER to celebrate.

It was only later that I found out what happened. Jake wasn't signaling me to bunt!

le was just brushing away a STICKER that had landed on his nose.

Over & out!

Wyatt

Illustrated by Mike Dammer

You'll Quack Up!
Can you help the waiter deliver this tray of food? There's just one path from START to FINISH. Once you've found it, write the letters along it in order in the spaces below to answer the riddle.
Answer on page 32
Start
O
B
L
U
U
T
P
L
A
O
N
Y
T
HONEY
N
A
A
E
26

P
T
L
E
I
I
B
I
M
MENU
L
B
Y
Y
A
O
T
S
E
L
M
O
T
O
I
Finish
What did the duck say when the meal arrived?
Illustrated by Sean Parkes

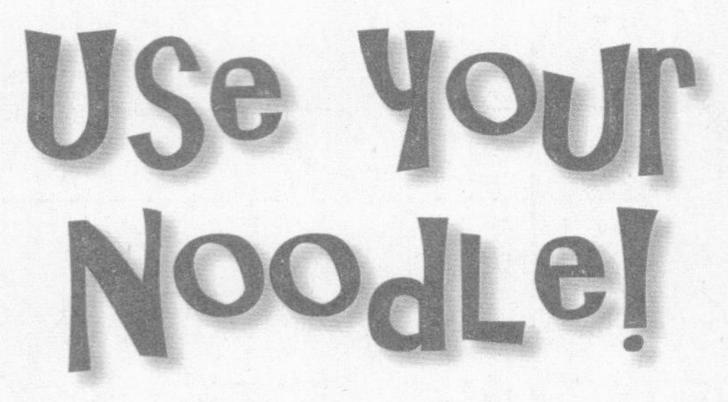

Use Your Noodle!

The names of **26** pasta shapes can fit into this grid. Use the number of letters in each word to figure out where each one belongs. Write in each word and cross it off the list as you go.

Answer on page 32

4 letters
ORZO
ZITI

5 letters
FIORI
PENNE

6 letters
ROTINI

7 letters
FUSILLI
GEMELLI
GNOCCHI
LASAGNE
PASTINA
~~**RAVIOLI**~~
ROTELLE

8 letters
COUSCOUS
FARFALLE
LINGUINE
RIGATONI

9 letters
CAPELLINI
MANICOTTI
RADIATORE
SPAGHETTI

10 letters
CANNELLONI
FETTUCCINE
TORTELLINI
VERMICELLI

11 letters
ORECCHIETTE
TAGLIATELLE

RAVIOLI
Illustrated by Brian White

ANSWERS

Front Cover
Look Again!

Back Cover Tic Tac Row

3 feathers on head ↘ · open beak ↓ · twig ↓ · yellow legs ↓

blue →

nest →

flying →

white breast ↗

Inside Cover Square Off!

PUMPKIN

CARROTS

BUTTERFLY

CLOWN FISH

They are all orange.

2–3 Start Your Engines

4 Pencil Paths

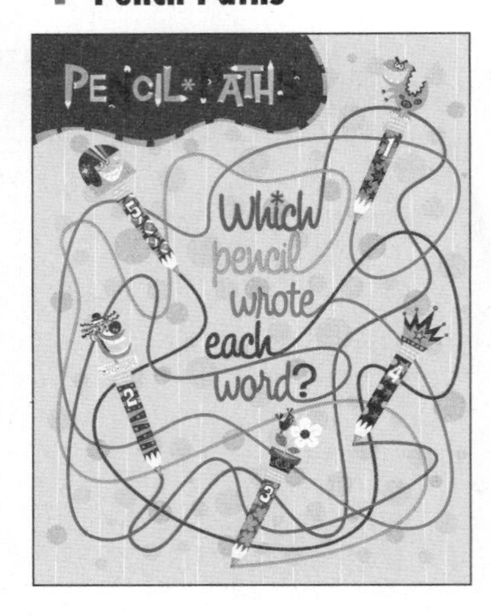

5 Word for Words

1. EMU
2. BUS
3. RAM
4. BARN
5. NEAR
6. RAIN
7. MANE
8. BEAM
9. MINUS
10. SIREN
11. NURSE
12. NUMBER

8 Nothing to It!

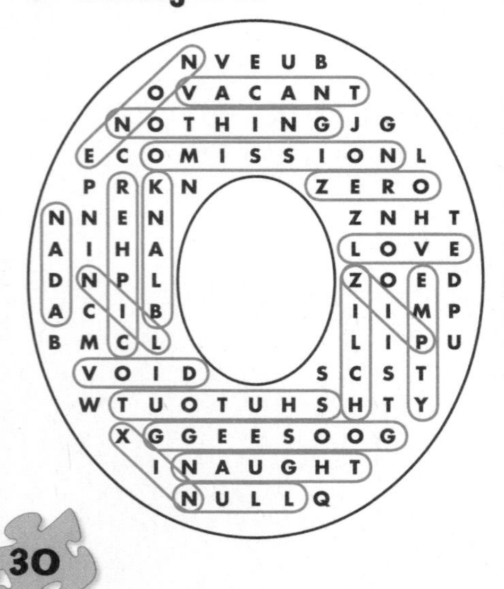

9 Add a Letter

BOOT /ROBOT
BEAR/ZEBRA
ACORN/CRAYON
MOLE/LEMON
SKATE/BASKET
BELT/TABLE
PEAR/PAPER
ROSE /HORSE
SCALE/ CASTLE
SALAD/SANDAL

10–11 Snow Kidding

2 State Your Name

13 Math Mirth

1. What is a math teacher's favorite dessert?
PUMPKIN PI

2. Which knight helped King Arthur build his round table?
SIR CIRCUMFERENCE

14–15 Disguise the Limit

6–17 Peanut Gallery

18 Map Mix-Up

Movie Palace—Sandwich Hut—Izzy's Ice Cream
Sim's Sweets—Archie's Arcade—T-Shirt Shack

9 The Text Big Thing

ello Maddie,
uess what? We are
rowing a big surprise
rthday party for your
ster! And your father
nd I need your help. We
eed you to text all her
ends about it. Oh, and
u can invite your
ends too! Surprise!
ve, Mom

20–21 Veggie Q's

To Market, to Market

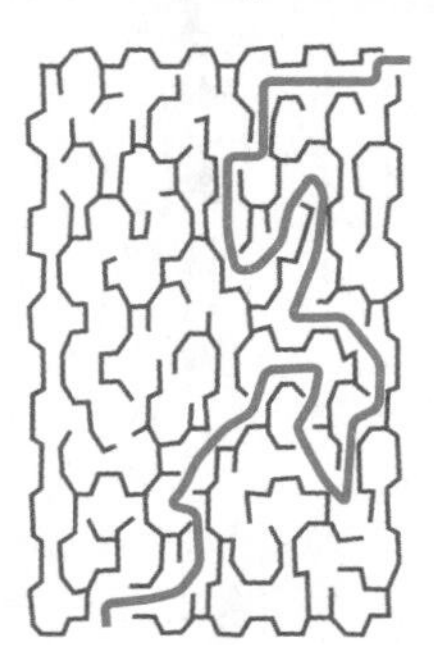

Veggies or Not?

Kale
Swiss Chard
Fennel
Okra
Jalapeño
Kohlrabi

Vegetable Soup

Carrot
Eggplant
Mushroom
Pumpkin

Hidden Veggies

Please trY A Marshmallow.
Could this BE ANy sillier?
This déCOR Needs to be updated.
An anteloPE Ambled by.
That BEE Tried to sting me!

Match Up

22–23 Feeling Antsy

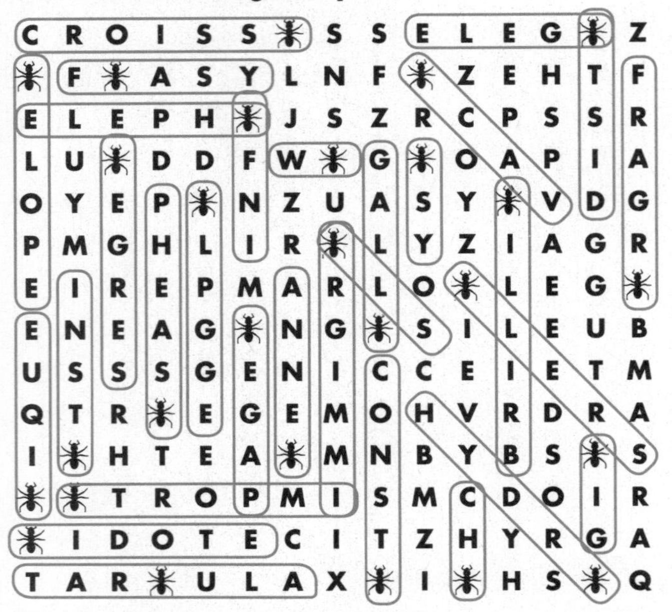

28–29 Use Your Noodle!

26–27 You'll Quack Up!

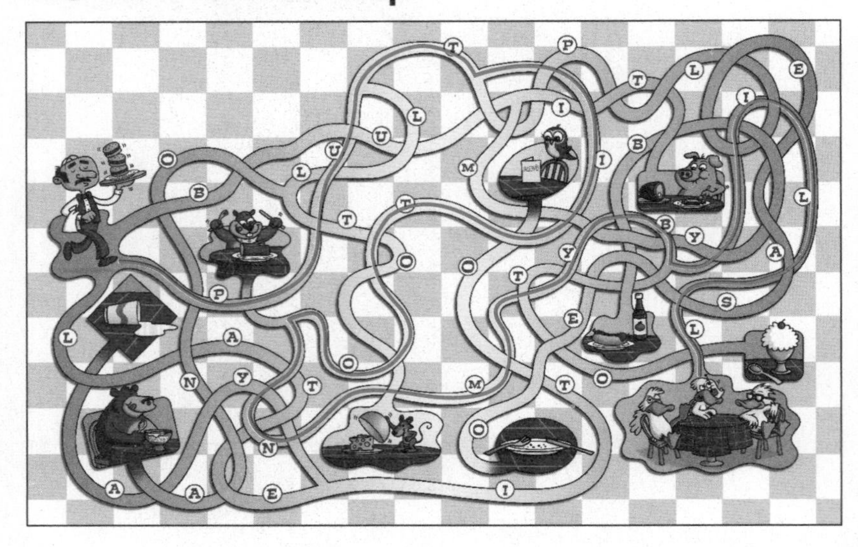

What did the duck say when the meal arrived?
PUT IT ON MY BILL.

Executive Editor: Mary-Alice Moore
Consulting Editor: Andrew Gutelle
Writer/Editor: Betsy Ochester
Art Director: Marta Ruliffson/Hey Kids!
Production Manager: Margaret Mosomillo

15 14 13 12 11 10 9

P.O. Box 18201
Columbus, OH 43218-0201

Cover and Text are SFI Certified